Hooray!

 Purrrfect

 Bee-utiful

 You did it!

 Grrreat

 Good Job

Fantastic!

Dino-mite

Purrrfect

 Bee-utiful

 Wonderful

Grrreat

 **Hooray!**

So Cool!

 You did it!

 Bee-utiful

 Dino-mite

 Fantastic!

 Purrrfect

 Good Job

 Good Job

 Grrreat

 Wonderful

 So Cool!

 You did it!

 Wonderful

 Dino-mite

So Cool!

 **Hooray!**

 Fantastic!

Decorate the number using your pencils.

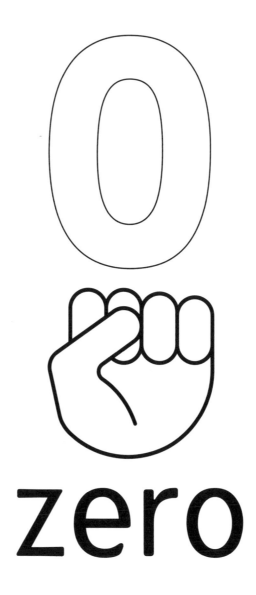

zero

Trace the numbers.

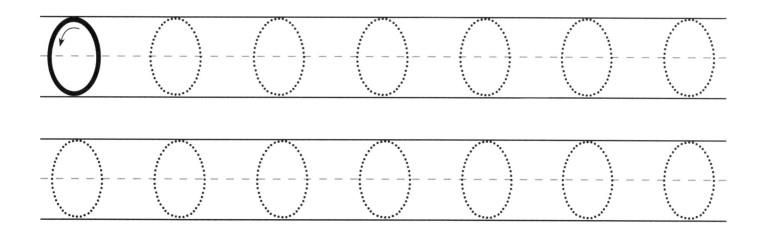

Circle the shoes with **0** laces.

Now decorate the pictures.

Shade the number using your pencils.

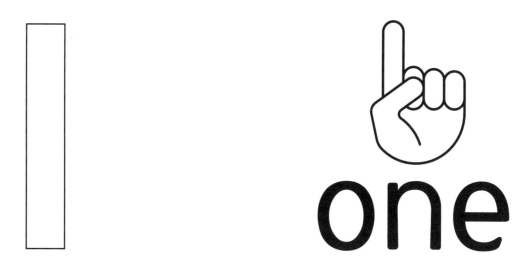

one

Trace the numbers.

Now decorate the pictures.

Circle the pictures with **1** window.

Now decorate the pictures.

4

Shade the number using your pencils.

two

Trace the numbers.

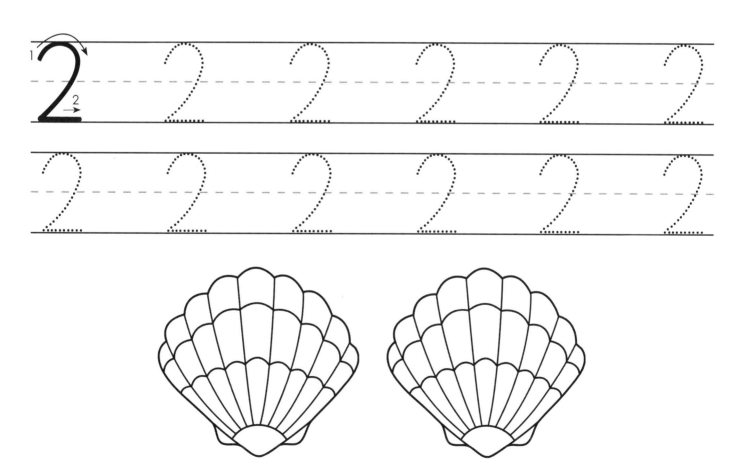

Now decorate the pictures.

Draw **2** dots on each of the ladybugs.

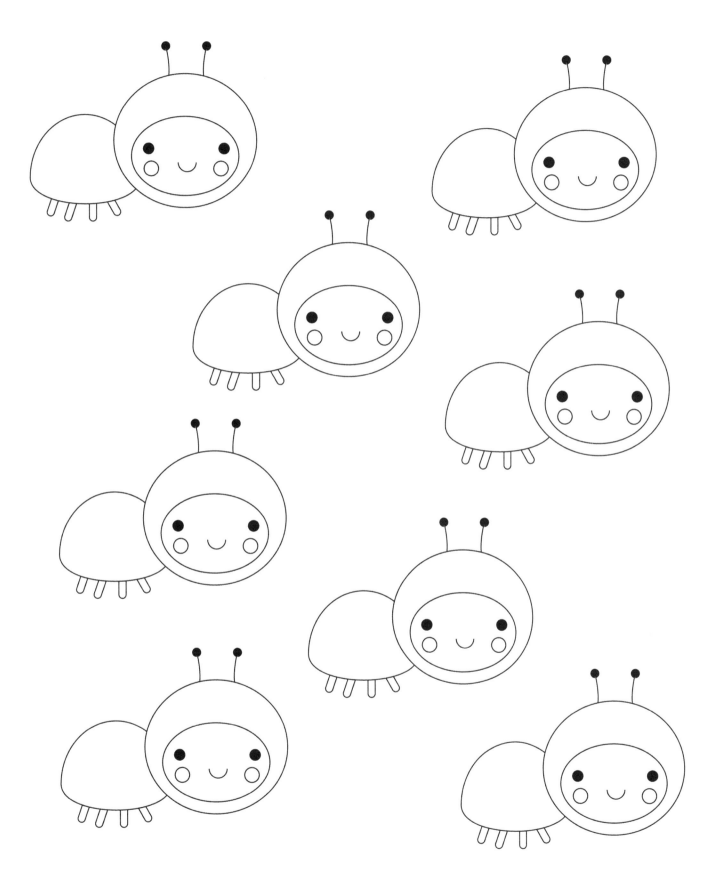

Now decorate the pictures.

Shade the number using your pencils.

three

Trace the numbers.

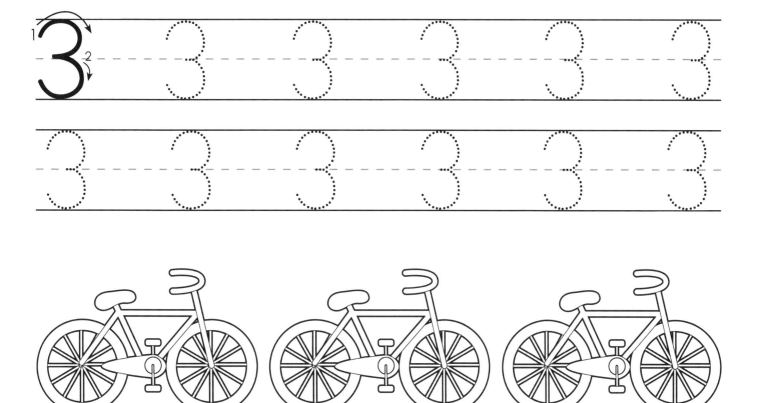

Now decorate the pictures.

Circle the group with **3**.

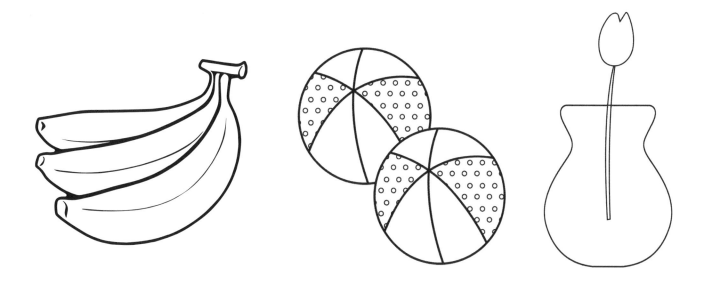

Draw **3** flowers in the vase.

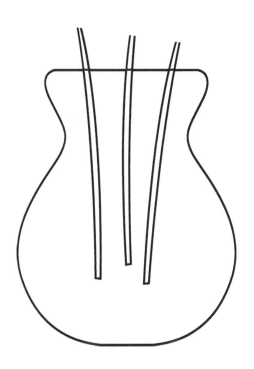

Now decorate the pictures.

Shade the number using your pencils.

four

Trace the numbers.

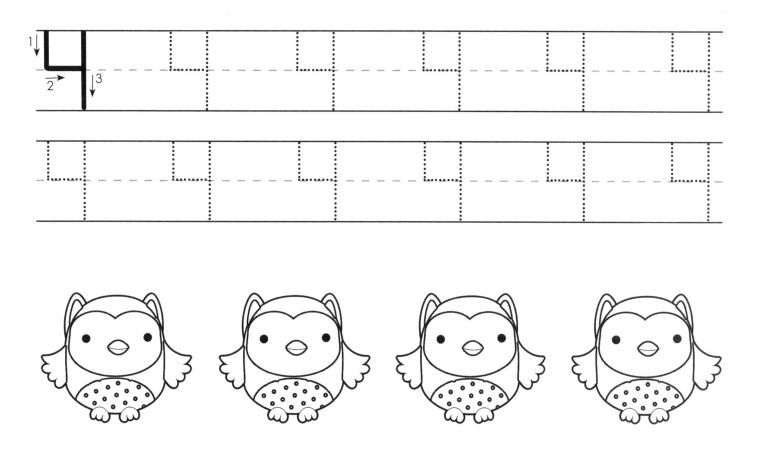

Now decorate the pictures.

Draw **4** stripes on each animal.

Draw **4** legs on each animal.

Now decorate the pictures.

Shade the number using your pencils.

five

Trace the numbers.

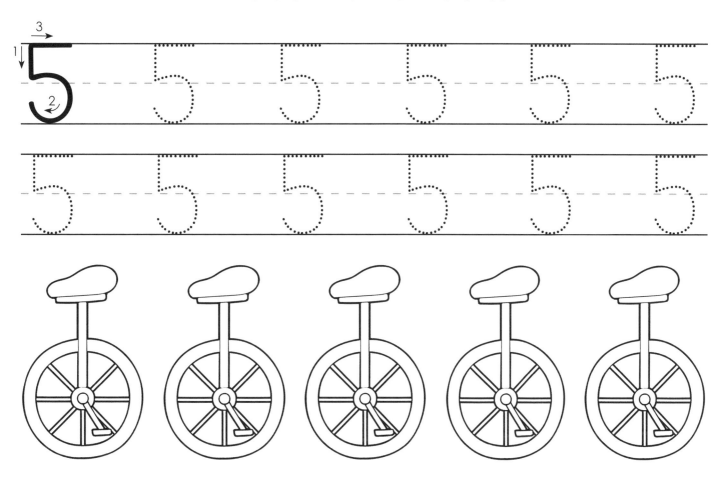

Now decorate the pictures.

Trace the **5** fish in the fish bowl.

Circle the flowers with **5** petals.

Now decorate the pictures.

Decorate the numbers and pictures.

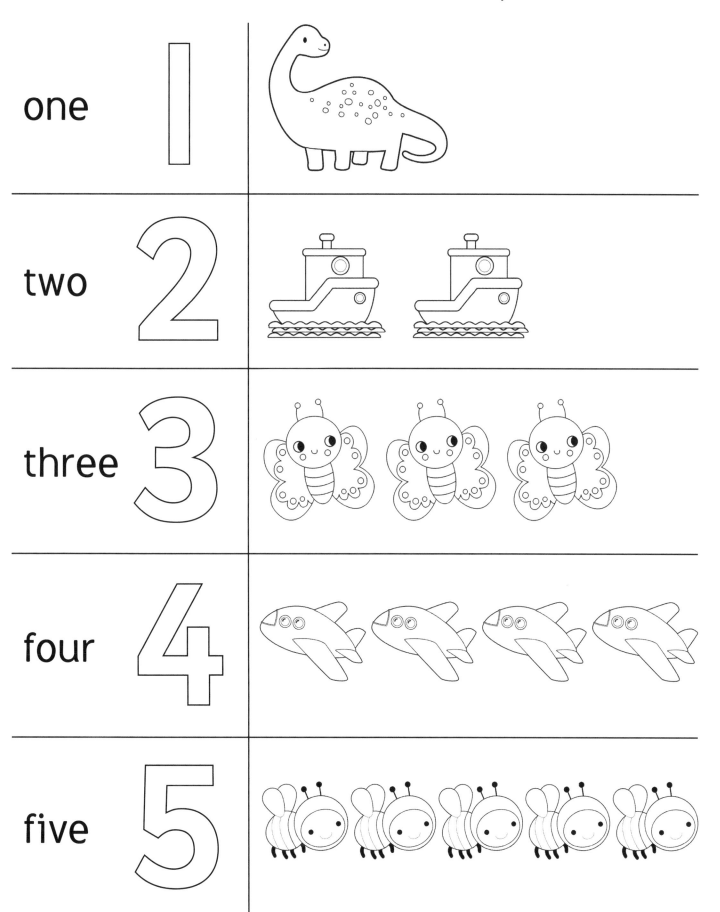

one | 1

two | 2

three | 3

four | 4

five | 5

Circle the number in each group.

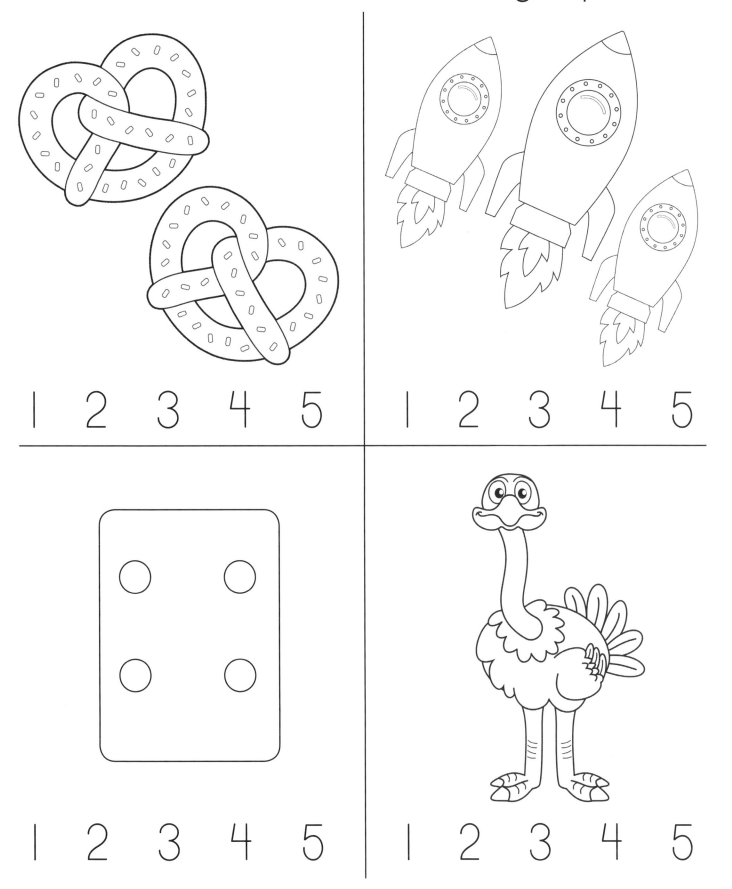

1 2 3 4 5

1 2 3 4 5

1 2 3 4 5

1 2 3 4 5

Now decorate the pictures.

14

Circle the number in each group.

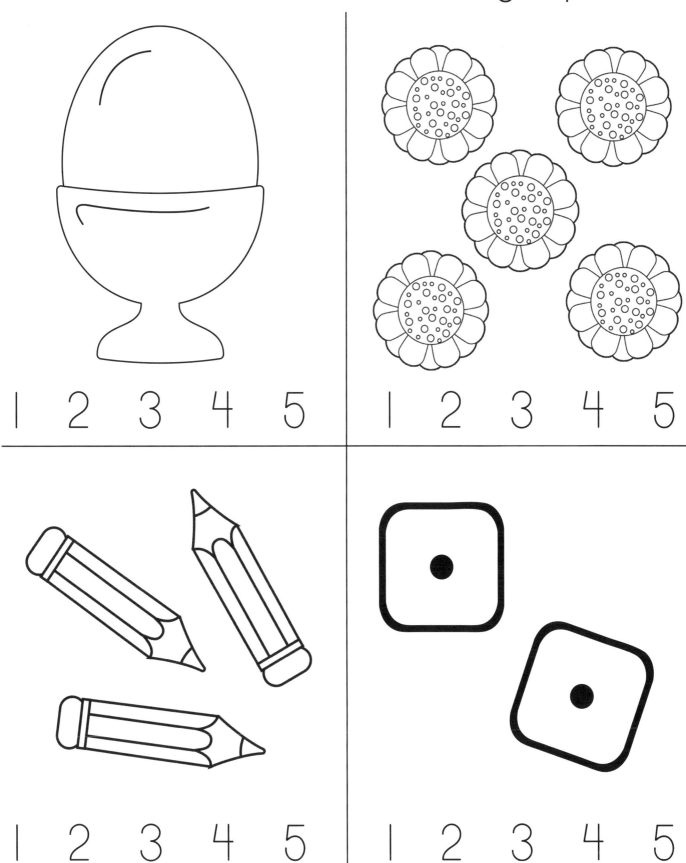

1 2 3 4 5

1 2 3 4 5

1 2 3 4 5

1 2 3 4 5

Now decorate the pictures.

Circle the cake with **4** candles.

Circle the jar with **0** lollies.

Now decorate the pictures.

Circle the butterfly with **4** dots.

Circle the dice with **5** dots.

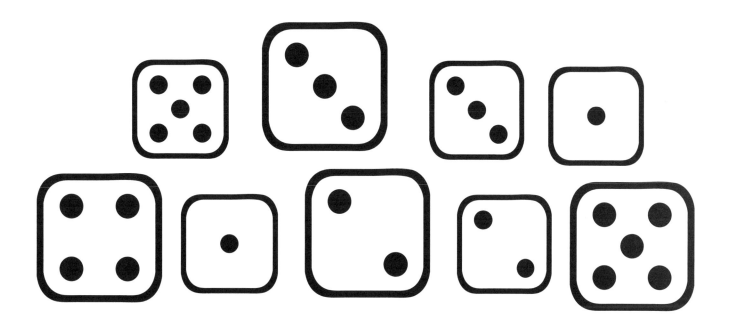

Now decorate the pictures.

Trace the number of dots that are on each card.

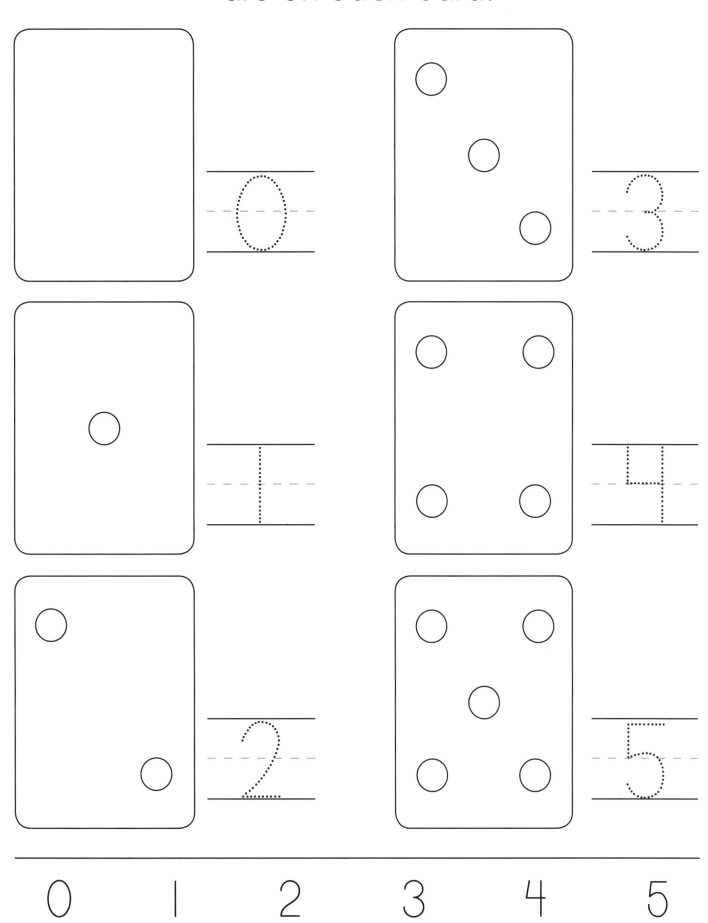

0   1   2   3   4   5

Write how many dots are on each card. The first one has been done for you.

3

1   2   3   4   5

Circle the groups of **5**.

Now decorate the pictures.

Circle the number that is **different**.

5   3   5   5

Circle the card that is **different**.

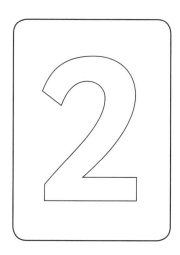 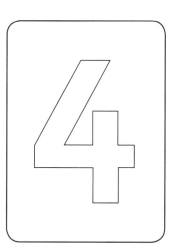 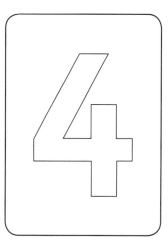 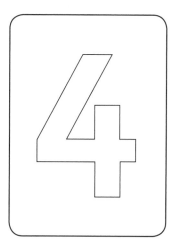

Circle the card that is **different**.

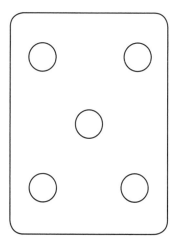 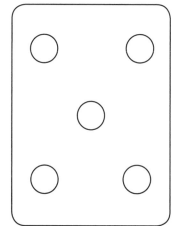 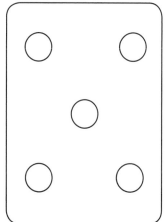 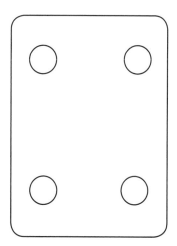

21

Shade the number using your pencils.

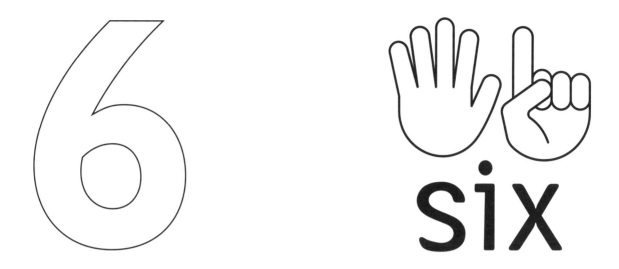

six

Trace the numbers.

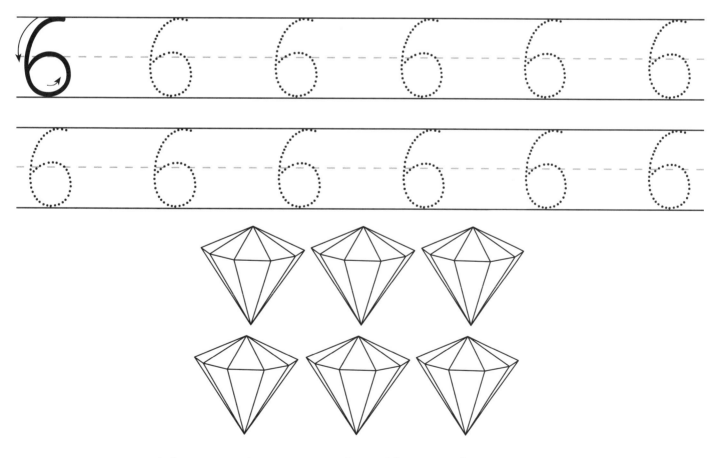

Now decorate the pictures.

Circle the stars with **6** points.

Now decorate the pictures.

Shade the number using your pencils.

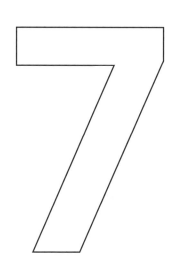

seven

Trace the numbers.

7

Now decorate the pictures.

Shade the **7** flies for the hungry frog.

Now shade the frog.

Shade the number using your pencils.

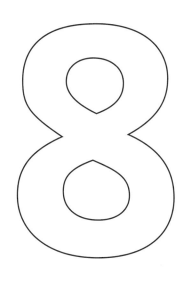

eight

Trace the numbers.

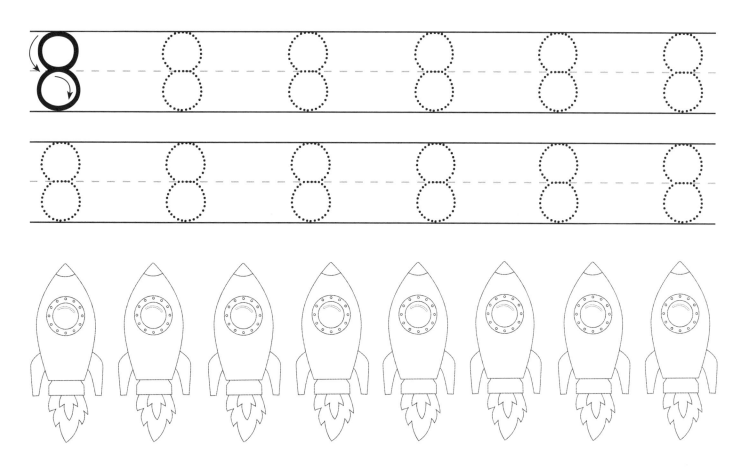

Now decorate the pictures.

Trace the **8** legs on the octopus.

Now shade the **8** starfish.

Shade the number using your pencils.

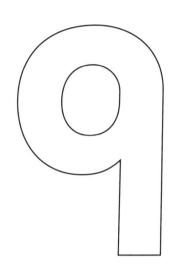

Trace the numbers.

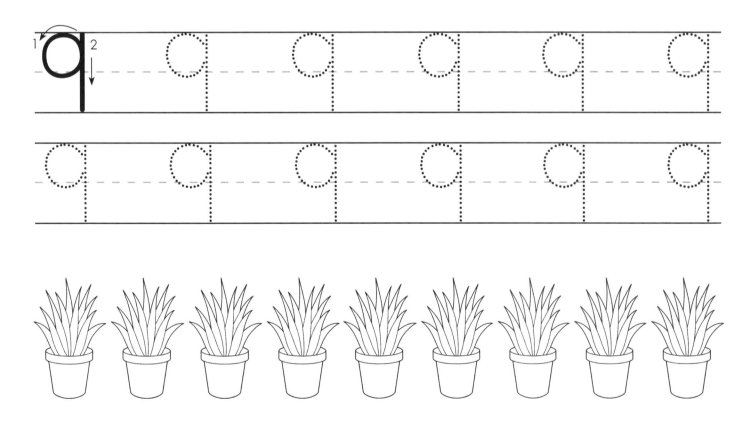

Now decorate the pictures.

Trace the path to the group with **9** worms.

Now decorate the pictures.

Shade the number using your pencils.

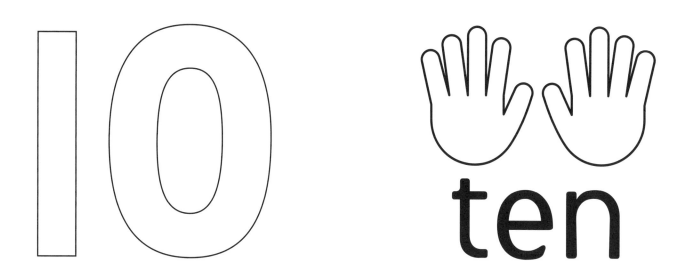

ten

Trace the numbers.

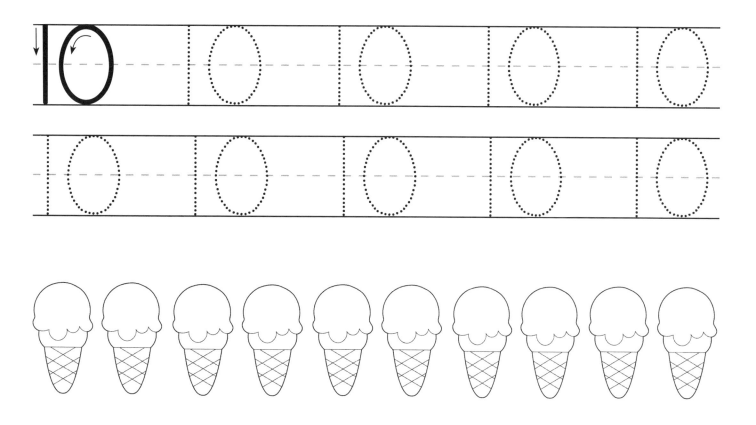

Now decorate the pictures.

Write the numbers **1 to 10** on the watch with missing numbers.

Now decorate the pictures.

Decorate the shapes using your pencils.

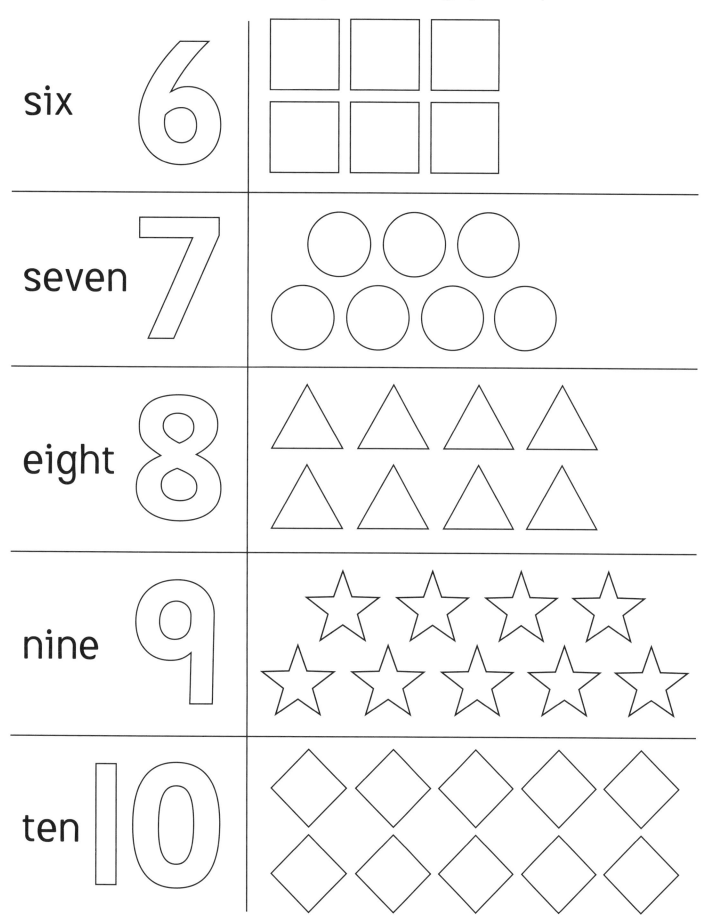

six 6

seven 7

eight 8

nine 9

ten 10

Circle the dinosaurs with **7** spots.

Now decorate the pictures.

Circle the number on each train that is **different**.

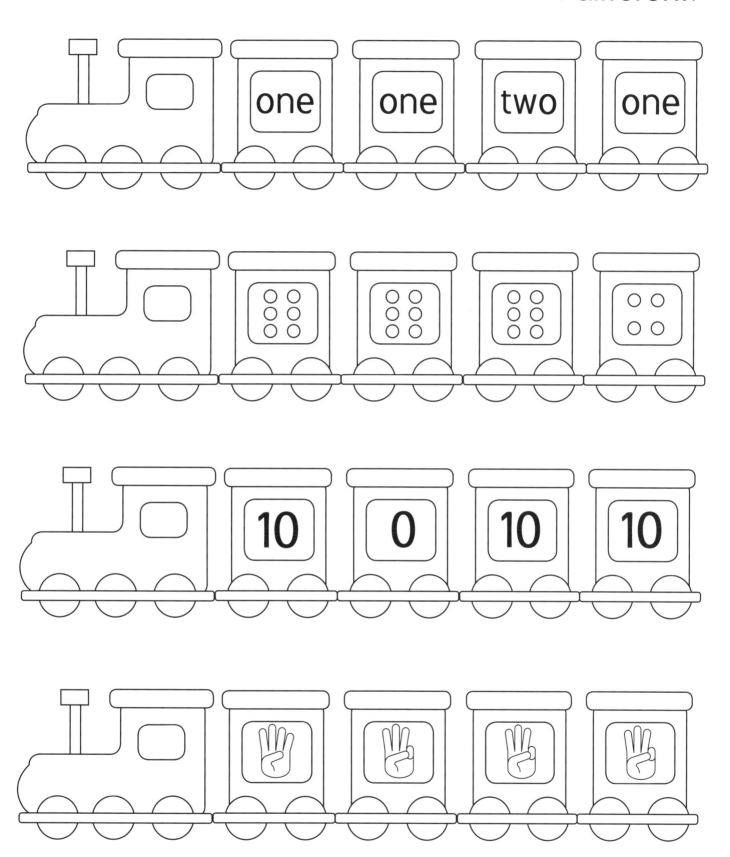

one one two one

Now decorate the pictures.

Circle all the shapes with **8** sides.

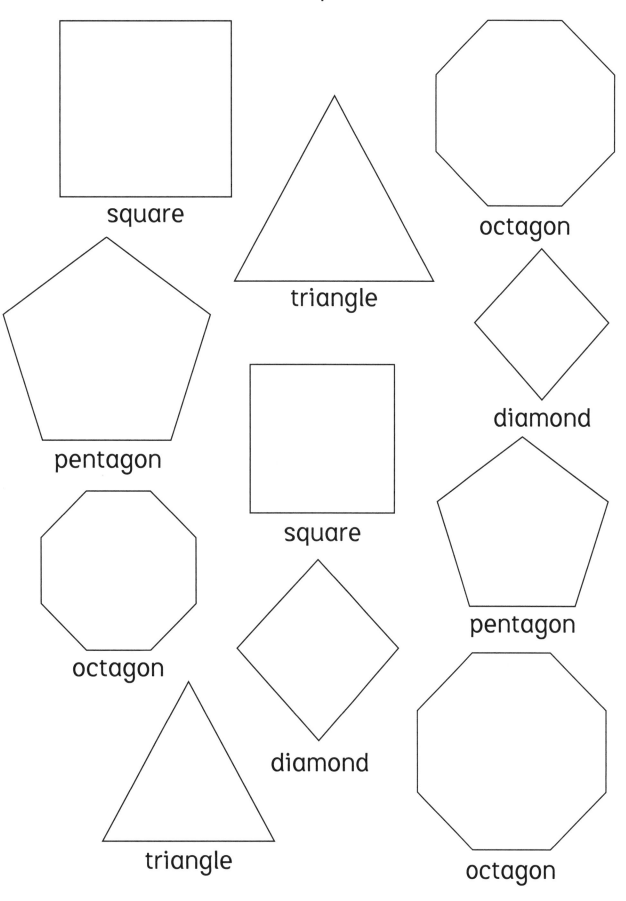

square

triangle

octagon

pentagon

diamond

square

octagon

pentagon

diamond

triangle

octagon

Now shade the shapes.

Circle the number in each group.

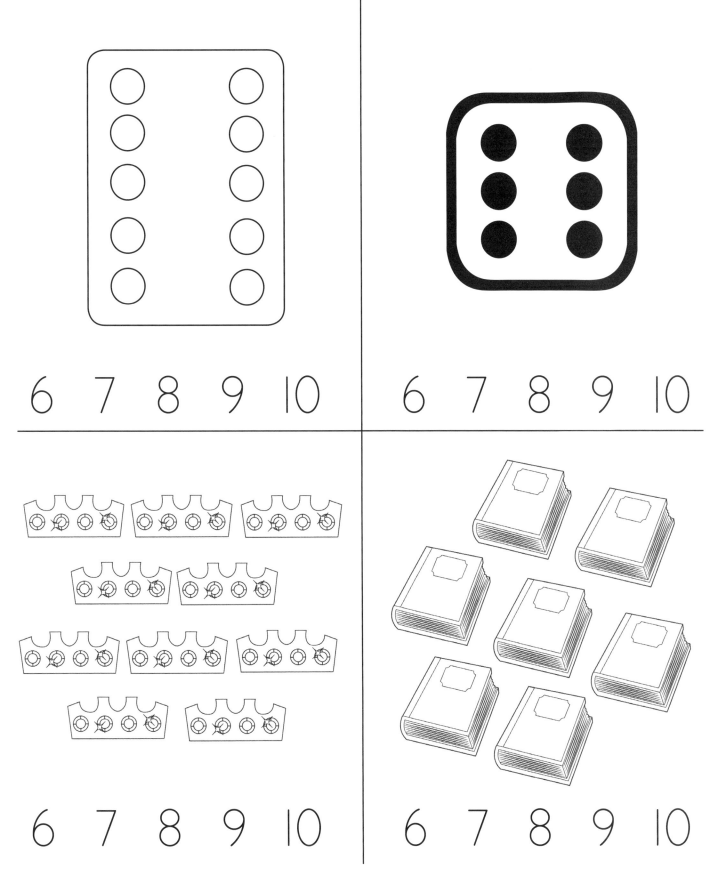

6 7 8 9 10

6 7 8 9 10

6 7 8 9 10

6 7 8 9 10

Now decorate the pictures.

Circle the number in each group.

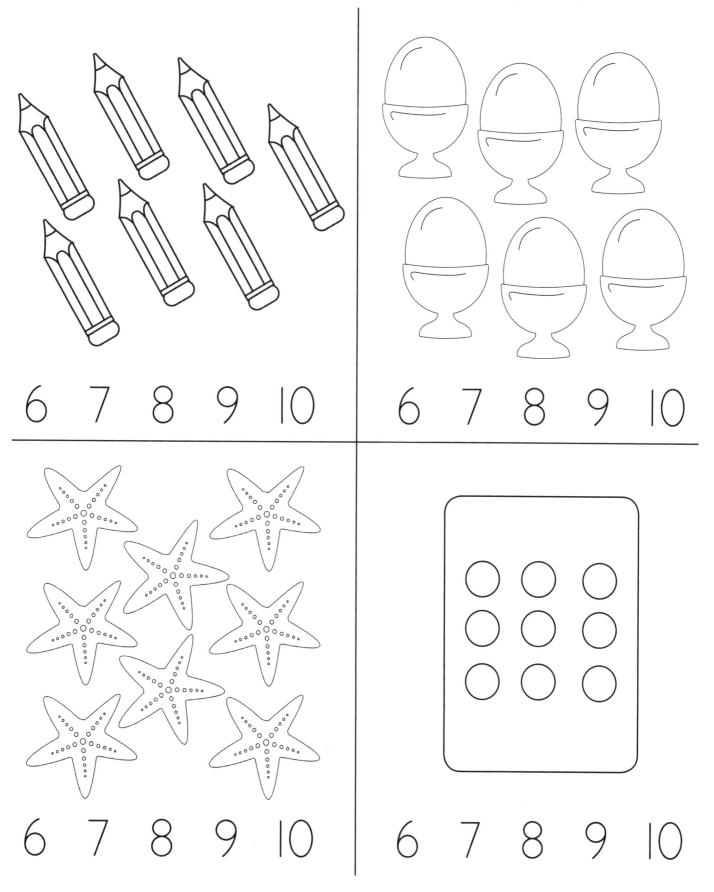

6 7 8 9 10

6 7 8 9 10

6 7 8 9 10

6 7 8 9 10

Now decorate the pictures.

Circle the castle with **2** flags.

Circle the hand that shows **5**.

Now decorate the pictures.

Circle the lamp with **9** stars.

Now decorate the pictures.

Write how many are in each group.

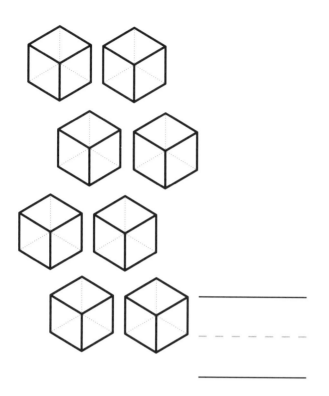

_____

- - - - - - - - -

_____

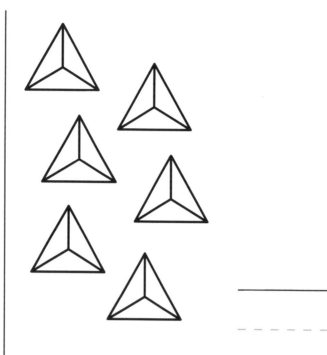

_____

- - - - - - - - -

_____

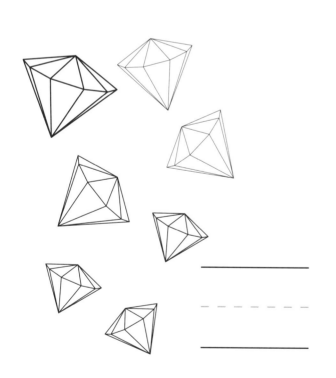

_____

- - - - - - - - -

_____

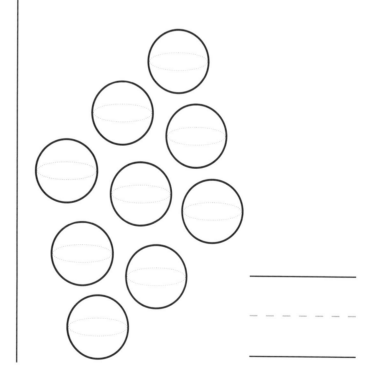

_____

- - - - - - - - -

_____

Now decorate the objects.

6   7   8   9   10

Write the numbers **1 to 10** on the caterpillar.

1 2 3 4 5 6 7 8 9 10

Now shade the picture.

Shade the 9 balloons.

Draw a line to match the numbers and the cards.

Circle the card that is **different**.

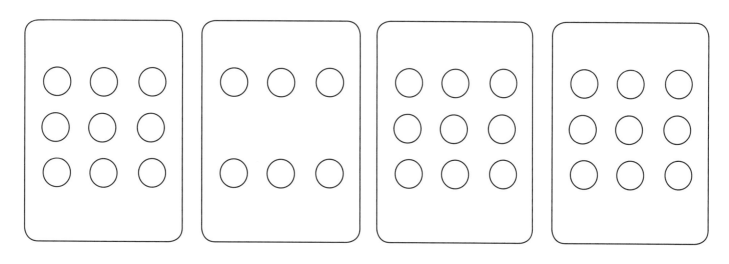

Circle the jumpers with **3** pictures on them.

Now decorate the pictures.

Circle the group with **8** animals.

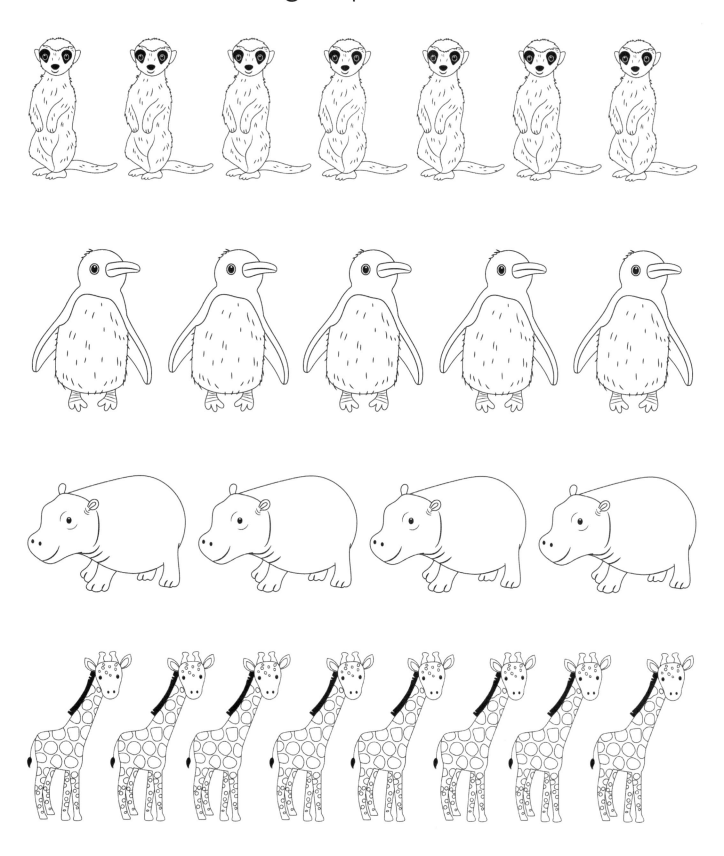

Now decorate the pictures.

Draw a line to match the numbers with the pictures.

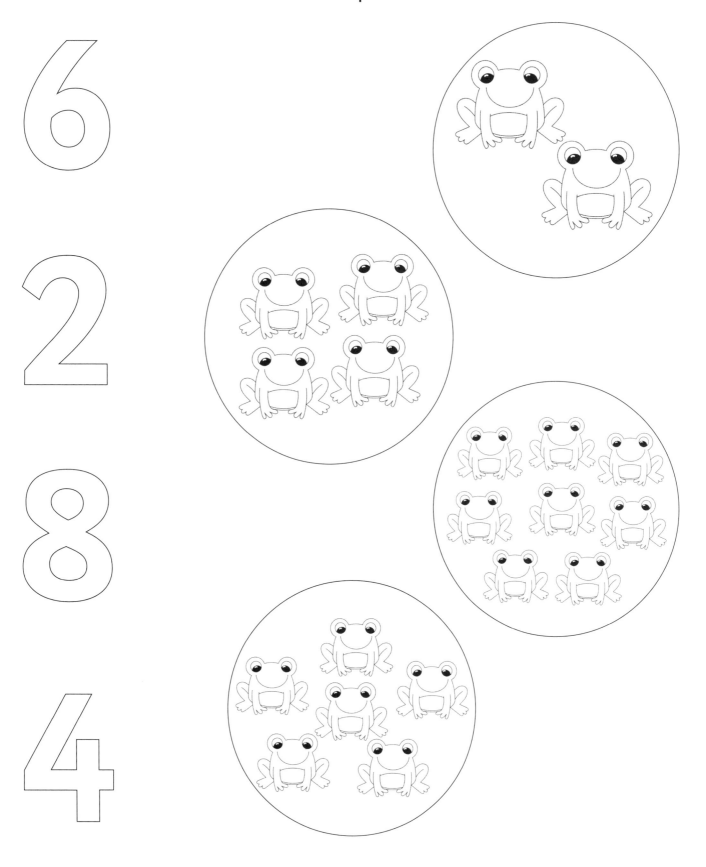

Now decorate the pictures.

Circle the group with **6** fruit.

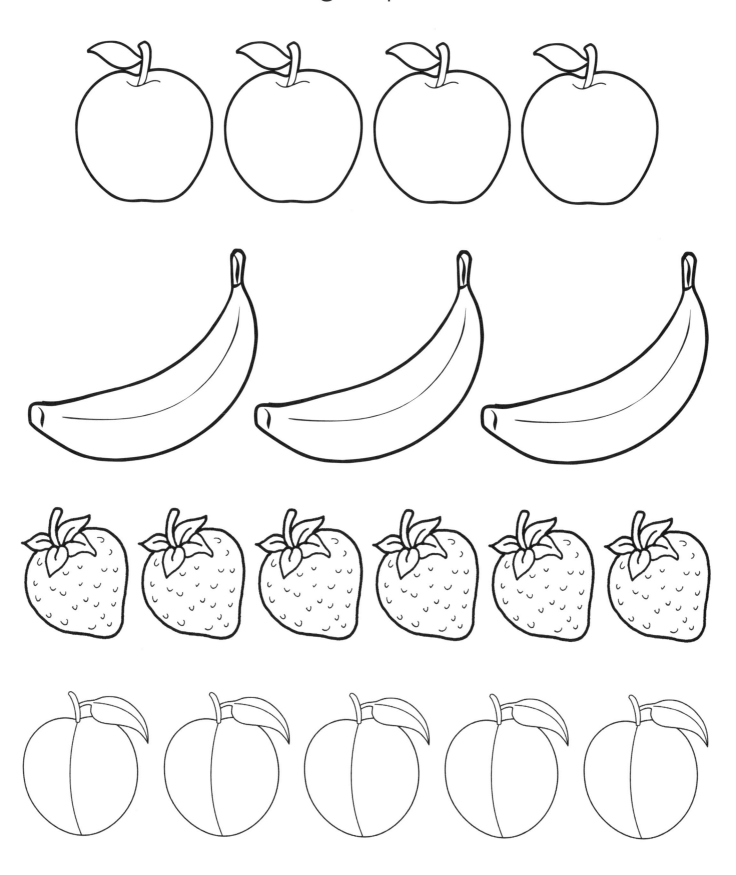

Now decorate the pictures.

Circle the groups with **4** insects.

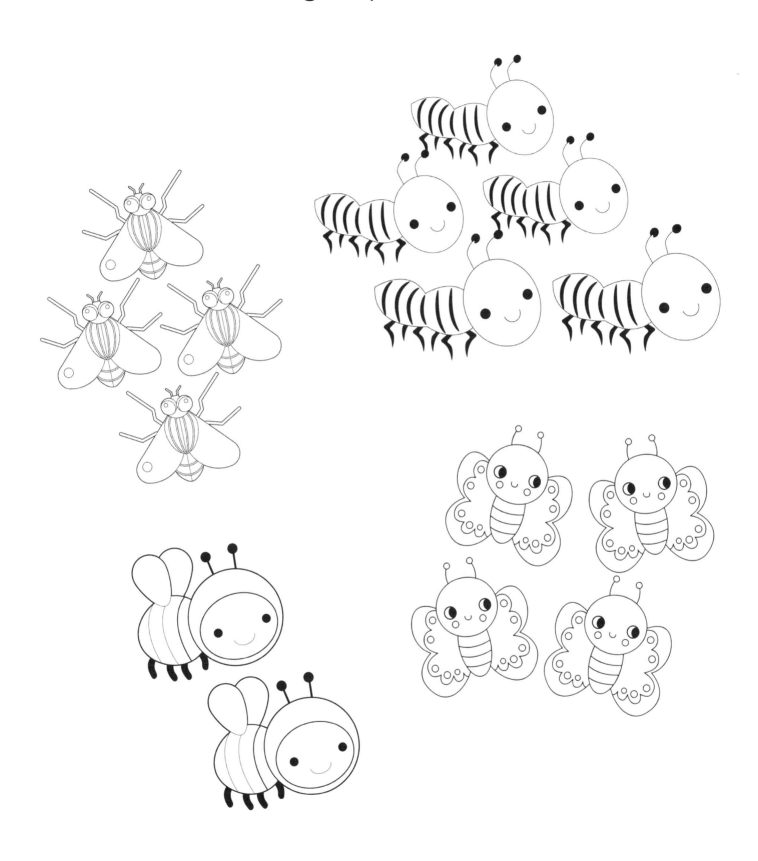

Now decorate the pictures.